Helicopters

A day at the sea

One morning Dad said,
"I'm going to take you all to the sea."

"That will be fun," said the children.
"Can we make a picnic?"

"Yes," said Dad. "Here's the picnic bag."

"Can I take my gingerbread man
with me?" asked Annie.

"What a baby!" Tom said.
"She wants to take her gingerbread man."

"I am not a baby!" said Annie.

"Just stop it," said Dad.
"Go and get in the car."

When they got to the sea,
Dan said, "I'm going to play."

"Me too!"

"Me too!"

"Don't go away, will you?" shouted Dad.
Dad sat reading his book and he
soon went to sleep.

"Look out there!" said Tom.
"What a funny thing! It's an old shed.
Let's go and see what's in it."

"... but Dad said we had to play here,"
said Annie.

"Don't be a baby!" Dan said.
"Dad can't see us now.
He went to sleep."

When the children were in the old shed,
they did not see that the sea
was coming in ... but Annie did.

"Come out. Quick!" she shouted.
"We have to get away from here."

"What is it now, baby?" they laughed.

"I am not a baby!" shouted Annie.
"Just you see."

"I'll run back and get Dad," said Annie.
"Dad will help."

"Get up, Dad. Quick," she shouted.
"The boys are out there
in that shed, and the sea is coming in."

Dad went and shouted to them.

"I'll go and get help.

Don't swim back.

Wait for help to come."

Dad ran to get help.
"Will you come and help my children?"
he asked. "The sea is coming in fast and
they can't get back."

"Yes, we'll help," said the men.
"We'll fly out in our helicopter
as fast as we can."

The men went out in the helicopter and
looked for the children.

"They are down there," one man said.

"They are in the old shed."

The men helped them into the helicopter.
"It's good to see you," said Dan.
"Now we'll fly back to your dad,"
the men said.

Soon the children were back with
Dad and Annie.

"It was Annie who came to get me,"
said Dad.

"You see," she said,
"I am not a baby, am I?"
And they all laughed.

What can helicopters do?

These animals want something to eat.
Can you guess who will help?

Look! A helicopter is coming
with something for the animals to eat.

Who will find this man?

He has to have help soon.

Here comes a helicopter.

It has come to help the man.

It will take him away.

A boy is in the water and
he can't swim. Who will help?

This helicopter will get him
out of the water.

The cars can't get down this street.

A helicopter sees the cars
and tells the radio.

Helicopters help all of us.